Hello Baby!
Record Book

Published by Ink Upon Paper
an imprint of Hinkler Books Pty Ltd
45–55 Fairchild Street
Heatherton Victoria 3202 Australia
www.hinkler.com

Text © Hinkler Books Pty Ltd 2004, 2010, 2011, 2015, 2019
Design © Hinkler Books Pty Ltd 2010, 2011, 2015, 2019

Author: Kate Cody
Illustration: Gina Maldonado
Cover design: Hinkler Studio
Prepress: Splitting Image

ISBN: 978 1 4889 1394 5

Printed and bound in China

Contents

Baby's Birth	4		Letter to Baby	27
Early Days at Home	6		2 Months Old	28
Naming Baby	8		4 Months Old	30
Baby's Family Tree	10		6 Months Old	32
Sleepy Nights	12		8 Months Old	34
Food to Grow	14		10 Months Old	36
Developmental Milestones	16		1 Year Old	38
Things Baby Loves	18		First Birthday	40
Fun with Water	20		First Holidays	42
Baby's Firsts	22		Looking Back	44
Healthy Baby	24		Milestone Cards	45
First Connections	26			

Baby's Birth

Name

....

Date of birth

....

Place of birth

....

....

Day of the week

....

Time of birth

....

Expected due date

....

Birth weight

....

Birth length

....

Head circumference

....

Delivered by

....

Name of doctor

....

Name of midwife

....

....

Birthing partners and helpers

....

Music or mantras during birth

....

About the birth

....

....

....

....

....

Baby looks like

....

....

....

....

....

Baby's eyes are

....

Baby's hair is

....

Baby's star sign

....

Visitors	Cards, flowers & presents	Memorable moments
....	....	....
....	....	....
....	....	....
....	....	....
....	....	....
....	....	....
....	....	....

"The happiest days are when babies come."
— MARGARET MITCHELL

Baby's birth photo

Early Days at Home

Visitors

....
....
....
....
....

Cards, flowers & presents

....
....
....
....

Memorable moments

....
....
....
....
....
....

Feeding Routine

Duration of feed

....
....
....
....
....

Description of feed

....
....
....
....

Sleeping Routine

Sleeping times

....
....
....
....
....

Waking times

....
....
....
....

"If you want your children to be intelligent, read them fairy tales. If you want them to be more intelligent, read them more fairy tales."

— ALBERT EINSTEIN

Welcome to the World

Our country's leader

....

News headlines

....

....

....

Popular songs

....

....

Popular TV shows

....

....

Movies showing at the cinema

....

....

Birth announcement card or photo

Memorable moments

....

....

....

....

Cost of a loaf of bread

....

Photo caption

....

....

....

....

Date photo taken

....

Naming Baby

Baby's name

....

....

Reason for choosing name

....

....

....

....

Other names considered

....

....

....

....

Nicknames

....

....

Photo caption

....

....

....

....

....

....

....

Date photo taken

....

Naming day photo

Naming Ceremony

Date

....

Place

....

Baby's outfit

....

Godparents or special people

....

Description of naming ceremony
and celebration

....

....

....

....

....

Who was there

....

....

....

....

....

....

What we ate

....

....

....

....

....

Cards and presents

....

....

....

....

....

*"The law of love could be best
understood and learned through
little children."*

– MAHATMA GANDHI

How baby behaved

....

....

....

....

Baby's Family Tree

All about my parents:

Name

....

Name

....

Date of birth

....

Date of birth

....

Place of birth

....

Place of birth

....

Life story in a nutshell

....
....
....
....
....
....

Life story in a nutshell

....
....
....
....
....
....

Important family dates

....
....
....
....
....

Brothers and sisters

....
....
....

Ages of brothers and sisters

....
....

Baby

Parent   Parent

Siblings

Aunties, Uncles   Aunties, Uncles
and Cousins   and Cousins

Grandparents   Grandparents

Great   Great
Grandparents   Grandparents

Other very special people in my life

One generation plants the trees; another gets the shade.

— CHINESE PROVERB

Sleepy Nights

Description of baby's nursery

....

....

....

....

....

Description of the cot/crib

....

....

....

....

....

First slept in cot/crib

....

....

First slept in own room

....

....

First slept through the night

....

....

Memorable moments

....

....

....

....

Helping Baby to Sleep

Evening routine

....

....

Lullabies that baby loves

....

....

Bedtime stories that baby loves

....

....

....

Bedtime toys or comforters

....

....

Settling techniques tried

....

....

"My biggest parenting conundrum: why is it so hard to put someone who is already sleepy to sleep."
– CHRISSY TEIGEN

"Hugs can do great amounts of good – especially for children."
– PRINCESS DIANA

Baby asleep

Favourite music around bedtime

....

....

Most successful settling technique

....

....

....

Photo caption

....

....

....

Date photo taken

....

Food to Grow

Food and Drink Firsts

First began eating puréed food

....

....

First began eating mashed food

....

....

....

"Children make you want to start life over."
— MUHAMMAD ALI

First began eating solid food

....

....

Foods that baby loves

....

....

Foods that baby doesn't like

....

....

First drank from a spout cup

....

....

First drank through a straw

....

....

First drank from a cup

....

....

First sat in a high chair

....

....

....

First ate with a spoon

....

....

First began sharing the family meal

....

....

Known food sensitivities

....

....

....

....

Memorable moments

....

....

....

....

Baby eating

Photo caption

....

....

....

....

....

Date photo taken

....

"The days are long, but the years are short."
– GRETCHIN RUBIN

Developmental Milestones

Began following with eyes

....
....
....

First smiled

....
....

Began putting rattle or toy to mouth

....
....

Began turning head to sound

....
....
....

Began grasping rattle or soft toy

....
....
....

First held up head

....
....
....

Photo caption

....
....
....

Date photo taken

....

Growing baby

First rolled over

....

....

First sat with support

....

....

Began to sit alone

....

....

First crawled

....

....

First stood with support

....

....

Began to walk with support

....

....

First stood unassisted

....

....

First pointed

....

....

First recognised self in a mirror

....

....

Started taking steps

....

....

Walked alone

....

....

....

....

First tooth

....

....

"Children learn to smile from their parents."
– SHINICHI SUZUKI

Things Baby Loves

Comforter

....
....
....
....

Things around home

....
....
....
....

Soft toys

....
....
....

Books

....
....
....
....

Toys

....
....

Nursery rhymes

....
....
....

Lullabies

....
....
....
....

Animals or pets

....
....
....
....

Games

....
....
....
....

Activities

....
....
....
....
....

People

....
....
....

Places

....
....
....
....

Photo caption

....
....
....
....

Date photo taken

....

Baby out and about

"Sometimes the smallest
things take up the most room
in your heart."
— WINNIE THE POOH

Fun with Water

Bathtime

First bath

....

....

....

First time in a big bath

....

....

....

Began sharing a bath

....

....

....

*"I was overcome with happiness,
love, and tenderness ... Right
after he was washed, I studied
him with my hands: his downy
little head, his little nose,
everything on the tiny body."*
— ANDREA BOCELLI

Bath toys

....

....

....

....

....

....

....

....

Bath games

....

....

....

....

....

....

Water Play

First trip to the beach or lake

....

....

First water play in garden

....

....

First splash in paddling pool

....

....

First dip in swimming pool

....

....

First swimming class

....

....

Baby's swimming costume

....

....

Photo caption

....

....

....

....

Date photo taken

....

"You see, Wendy, when the first baby laughed for the first time, its laugh broke into a thousand pieces, and they all went skipping about, and that was the beginning of fairies."
– J.M. BARRIE

Baby in the bath

Baby's Firsts

First picked up tiny objects

....

First stacked blocks

....

First turned the pages of a book

....

First waved goodbye

....

First haircut

....

First played peek-a-boo

....

First put on their own clothes

....

First clapped hands

....

First pulled a pull-along toy

First danced

....

Other baby firsts

....
....
....
....
....
....
....
....
....
....

"Children are the living messages we send to a time we will not see."
–JOHN F. KENNEDY

22

Clever baby

Photo caption

....

....

....

....

....

Date photo taken

....

"The soul is healed by being with children."
-FYODOR DOSTOEVSKY

Healthy Baby

Name of maternal and child
health nurse

....

Maternal and child health
appointments

....

....

....

....

....

....

....

....

....

....

Name of doctor

....

Baby's immunisation dates

....

....

....

....

....

....

....

....

....

....

Other special trips to the doctor

....

....

....

"Love as powerful as your
mother's for you, leaves its
own mark. To have been loved
so deeply... will give us some
protection forever."

—J.K. ROWLING

Photo caption

Date photo taken

....

....

....

....

....

....

"You are the bows from which your children as living arrows are sent forth."

–KHALIL GIBRAN

Happy, healthy baby

First Connections

First cooed

....

....

First laughed

....

....

Started babbling

....

First joined in singing a song

....

....

First said "Mama!"

....

First said "Dada!"

....

To every child – I dream of a
world where you can laugh,
dance, sing, learn, live in peace
and be happy.
–MALALA YOUSAFZAI

First time baby said own name

....

....

First word

....

....

New words   Date

....

....

....

....

....

....

....

....

....

....

....

....

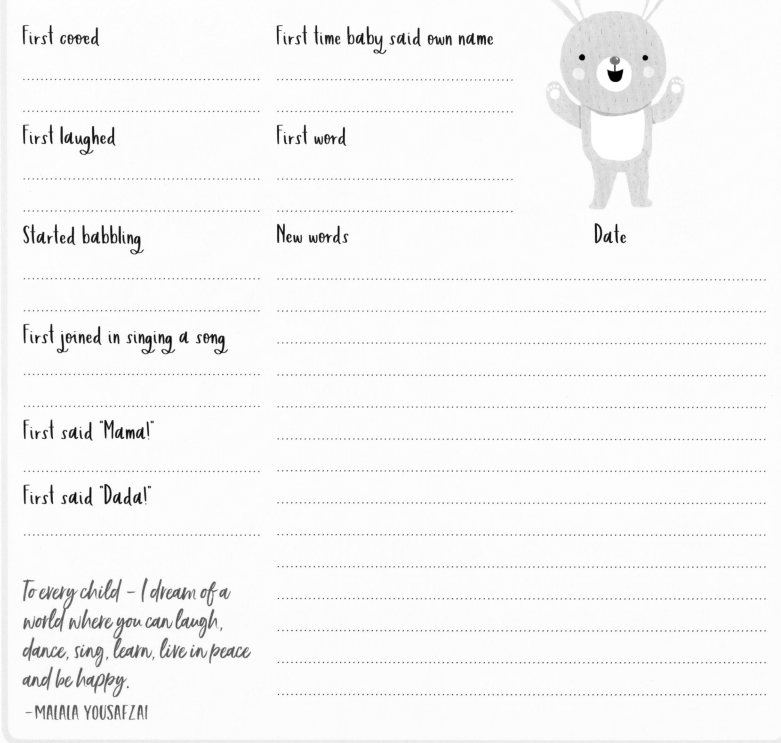

Letter to baby

Use this space to write a letter to baby that you can share with them when they're older.

2 Months Old

Usually woke for the day at

....

....

Went to bed for the day at

....

....

Daytime sleep routine

....

....

....

Daytime feeding routine

....

....

Night-time sleeping
and feeding routine

....

....

Weight

....

Length

....

Head circumference

Crying periods

....

....

....

....

Best way to calm baby

....

....

....

....

Changes

....

....

....

New sounds

....

....

....

*"Every baby born into the world
is a finer one than the last."*

—CHARLES DICKENS

Baby at 2 months

New firsts

....
....
....
....

Baby's temperament

....
....
....

Nicknames

....
....
....

Description of a typical day

....
....
....

Photo caption

....
....
....
....
....

Date photo taken

....

4 Months Old

Usually woke for the day at

....
....
....

Went to bed for the day at

....
....
....

Daytime sleep routine

....
....

Daytime feeding routine

....
....
....

Night-time sleeping
and feeding routine

....
....
....

Photo caption

....
....
....
....

Date photo taken

....

Baby at 4 months

Weight

....

Length

....

Head circumference

....

Crying periods

....

....

....

Time spent playing on the floor

....

....

Best way to calm baby

....

....

Changes

....

....

....

New sounds

....

....

New firsts

....

....

Baby's temperament

....

....

....

Nicknames

....

"Every child begins
the world again."
-HENRY DAVID THOREAU

Description of a typical day

....

....

....

....

Preferred activities

....

....

....

Preferred foods

....

....

6 Months Old

Usually woke for the day at

....

....

Went to bed for the day at

....

....

Daytime sleep routine

....

....

Daytime feeding routine

....

....

....

"The best kind of parent you can be is to lead by example."
—DREW BARRYMORE

Night-time sleeping and feeding routine

....

....

....

....

Weight

....

Length

....

Head circumference

....

Time spent playing on the floor

....

....

Crying periods

....

....

....

Best way to calm baby

....

....

Changes

....

....

....

New teeth

....

....

....

Teething symptoms and remedies

....

....

....

New sounds

....

....

New firsts

....

....

....

Baby's temperament

....

....

....

Nicknames

....

....

Description of a typical day

....

....

....

Baby at 6 months

Preferred activities

....

....

....

Preferred foods

....

....

Photo caption

....

....

....

....

....

Date photo taken

....

8 Months Old

Usually woke for the day at

....
....

Went to bed for the day at

....
....
....

Daytime sleep routine

....
....

Daytime feeding routine

....
....

Night-time sleeping
and feeding routine

....
....
....
....

Photo caption

....
....

Date photo taken

....

Baby at 8 months

Weight

....

Length

....

Head circumference

....

Time spent playing on the floor

....

....

Crying periods

....

....

Best way to calm baby

....

....

Changes

....

....

....

New teeth

....

....

....

Teething symptoms and remedies

....

....

....

New sounds

....

....

New firsts

....

....

Baby's temperament

....

....

Nicknames

....

....

Description of a typical day

....

....

....

Preferred activities

....

....

....

Preferred foods

....

....

....

"A new baby is like the
beginning of all things –
wonder, hope, a dream
of possibilities."
—EDA J. LESHAN

10 Months Old

Usually woke for the day at

....

....

Went to bed for the day at

....

....

Daytime sleep routine

....

....

Daytime feeding routine

....

....

"A person's a person,
no matter how small."
–DR. SEUSS

Night-time sleeping
and feeding routine

....

....

....

....

Weight

....

Length

....

Head circumference

....

Time spent playing on the floor

....

Crying periods

....

....

....

Best way to calm baby

....

....

Changes

....

....

New teeth

....

....

Teething symptoms and remedies

....

....

....

New sounds

....

....

New firsts

....

....

....

Baby's temperament

....

....

....

Baby at 10 months

Nicknames

....

....

Description of a typical day

....

....

....

....

Preferred activities

....

....

....

Preferred foods

....

....

....

Photo caption

....

....

....

....

Date photo taken

....

1 Year Old

Usually woke for the day at

....

....

Went to bed for the day at

....

....

Daytime sleep routine

....

....

Daytime feeding routine

....

....

Night-time sleeping
and feeding routine

....

....

....

....

Photo caption

....

....

....

Date photo taken

....

....

Baby at 1 year old

Weight

....

Length

....

Head circumference

....

Time spent playing on the floor

....

....

Crying periods

....

....

Best way to calm baby

....

....

Changes

....

....

....

New teeth

....

....

....

Teething symptoms and remedies

....

....

....

New sounds

....

New firsts

....

....

Baby's temperament

....

....

Nicknames

....

....

Description of a typical day

....

....

....

Preferred activities

....

....

Preferred foods

....

....

"Until you have a baby, you don't even realise how much you were missing one."
—JODI PICOULT

First Birthday

Date of birthday celebration

....

How it was celebrated

....

....

Who was there

....

....

....

....

Photo caption

....

....

Date photo taken

....

First birthday

Your present to baby

....
....
....
....
....

Other presents

....
....
....
....
....

Baby's outfit

....
....
....

How baby behaved

....
....

Baby's reaction when
'Happy Birthday' sung

....
....
....
....
....

Description of cake

....
....
....
....

Description of birthday
celebration

....
....
....
....

Memorable moments

....
....
....
....
....
....
....

*"Children reinvent your
world for you."*
–SUSAN SARANDON

First Holidays

First Holiday Season or Trip

People present

....
....
....
....
....

Location

....
....
....
....
....

Getting there details

....
....

Toys and books enjoyed

....
....
....

Baby's holiday routine

....
....
....

New experiences

....
....
....
....
....

"The best way to make children good is to make them happy."
—OSCAR WILDE

Holiday highlights

....
....
....
....
....

Memorable moments

....
....
....
....
....

On holiday

Other Holidays

Holiday highlights

....

....

....

Memorable moments

....

....

Photo caption

....

....

....

....

....

Date photo taken

....

Looking Back

Baby's First Year

Greatest pleasure

....
....
....
....
....
....

Greatest challenge

....
....
....
....
....
....

Siblings' early reaction to baby

....
....
....
....
....
....
....

Siblings' relationship with baby now

....
....
....
....
....
....

Baby's personality

....
....
....
....

Thoughts on being a family

....
....
....

Milestone Cards

Today I was

born

Today I am

1

Month Old

Today I am

3

Months Old

Today I am

6

Months Old

Milestone Cards

Today I am

8

Months Old

Today I am

10

Months Old

Today I am

1

Year Old

Last night I

slept through the night

Milestone Cards

Today I
rolled over

Today I
crawled

Today I
sat up
by myself

Today I
stood up

Milestone Cards

Today I
walked
for the first time

Today I
ate solids
for the first time

Today I said my
first
word

Me
and my
family